THE FIRST SEVEN YEARS

A Record Book for Mother and Child

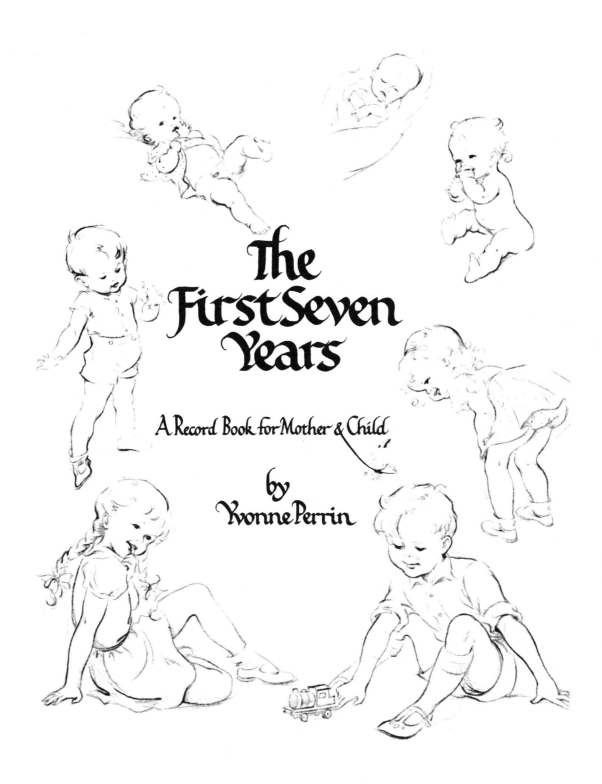

The First Seven Years

A Record Book for Mother & Child

by
Yvonne Perrin

A & C Black · London

First published in 1950 by A & C Black (Publishers) Ltd
35 Bedford Row, London WC1R 4JH
Reprinted 1977, 1979, 1983, 1988, 1991

ISBN 0-7136-0597-9

© 1950 A & C Black (Publishers) Ltd

Printed and bound in Great Britain
by Hollen Street Press Ltd, Slough, Berkshire

CONTENTS

Introduction 6

Record of Birth 9

Measurements at Birth 11

The Christening 15

At Three Months 19

At Six Months 25

At Nine Months 31

First Birthday 36

Chart of Baby's Weight 41

Baby's Teeth 43

First Steps 47

At Eighteen Months 51

Second Birthday 57

Third Birthday 59

Fourth Birthday 61

Fifth Birthday 63

Sixth Birthday 65

Seventh Birthday 67

Health Record 72

School Record 74

First Writing and Drawing 75

Funny Sayings and Incidents 76

Favourite Books 77

Pets and Playmates 78

Favourite Games 79

Prayers 80

INTRODUCTION

BABY days are short and quickly forgotten and the details of these precious moments are lost all too soon in the excitement of growing up. At the time a mother cannot realise she will ever forget even the smallest event in the life of her baby. This book has been planned for you to record briefly the details of your baby's first seven years.

The psychology book has, to some extent, taken the place of years of experience, but a "mother's instinct" which has come to her down the ages is valuable knowledge, and coupled with her own common sense should not be despised. The method that was so successful with one child may well be a complete failure with another, but while methods may change the foundations of good mothercraft never alter.

They will always be serenity, humour, affection and understanding, and in a mother's protective care and love the fragile bundle of helplessness will grow into a healthy, happy child.

Too often there is so much to do, a mother cannot find the time to watch the rapid growth and complex changes through which her baby is passing. She would like a little longer time to enjoy the experience of helping him to independence. By your entries in this book you will recapture the delights of babyhood.

But a record must be accurate, and to be of real use, the events should be entered at the time of their occurrence. Then you will be able to look back upon all the little things, as well as the special events, which will become dearer as the years pass, and illustrated throughout with photographs and snapshots this book will be a fascinating reminder; a treasured possession always, recalling the fun and responsibility of being a parent.

BABY'S RECORD BOOK

IN the first days of life a baby usually loses a few ounces and regains birth weight by the tenth day. The average weight of an infant at birth is seven and a half pounds, but if baby is much overweight or underweight he will tend to come down or go up to the average in the course of the first few months.

The length of the average baby boy at birth is twenty one inches, and that of a baby girl slightly less.

Undoubtedly the most suitable food for baby is the mother's milk, nothing else can quite replace it to satisfy his hunger for nourishment and comfort. In his mother's arms he feels secure and confident, and taking his food under the best possible conditions, he will have no nervous troubles to add to any possible digestive disturbance.

8

ANNOUNCEMENT

Born on   the   day of   19

At   at   m

To

        Doctor   Nurse

            Grandparents

Gifts

9

With a little preparation nearly every mother can nurse her baby and every effort should be made to do so, but if, inspite of all her efforts it is impossible, modified cow's milk is the best substitute. Given in the right way and with confidence by the one person he loves and trusts the average baby will take quite happily to bottle feeding with very excellent results.

Nearly all babies will do very well on five feeds in the twenty four hours, given four hourly at 6am, 10am, 2pm, 6pm and 10pm. A baby weighing under six pounds at birth will probably require three hourly feeding at 6am, 9am, 12noon, 3pm, 6pm and 10pm until he weighs about 8lbs, when the feeds can gradually be changed to four hourly, but the total amount given during the twenty four hours is not necessarily more.

Baby may cry from thirst without being actually hungry. A drink from a spoon or bottle of cool boiled water or of orange juice suitably diluted will keep him contented between feeds.

A regular routine is most important and promotes good digestion and sound sleep. Feeds, sleep and bath should take place as far as possible at the same time each day, and with calm but firm persistence baby can be trained to regular habits.

10

MEASUREMENTS AT BIRTH

Weight

Length

Circumference of Head

Chest Measurement

After food, rest and quiet are baby's greatest need. From birth to two months he should sleep twenty hours out of the twenty four. He also needs plenty of fresh air and should sleep out of doors all day winter and summer. The only weather which is really unsuitable for baby is fog.

Apart from hunger or thirst and pain there are two other things of which a newborn baby is conscious, loud noises and a fear of being dropped. Speak softly to him and handle him gently but firmly he loves to feel he is in safe hands.

Some crying during childhood is inevitable, it is baby's only language. A tiny infant may be left to cry for a little while before he goes to sleep, but crying is a habit more easily started than stopped and should be avoided where possible. Then as he grows older self control will become habitual, and frustrations and even disappointments will be accepted cheerfully.

COLOURING

Colour of Eyes at Birth

Later

Colour of Hair

Brows

Lashes

Complexion

BABY'S FIRST PHOTOGRAPH

BABY WAS NAMED

On the   day of   19

At

In the Presence of

Gifts

SNAPSHOTS

16

BABY'S FIRST CURL

Cut on the   day of   19

Age

Arrange the curl in
a cellophane envelope
and paste in position.

THE FIRST THREE MONTHS

BY the third month the average baby is about four pounds over birth weight and the gain of weight is a very good indication of baby's progress. Weigh your baby every week for the first three months and fortnightly after that. Little ups and downs in weight do not usually matter, but it is better for the increase to be gradual and steady.

Exercise is quite as important to baby's development as fresh air. A very young baby will exercise himself if left free to move about. Of his own accord he will kick and splash in his bath, or push hard with his feet against his mother's hand. Let baby lie on your lap after a meal to kick and play with your fingers, but be careful not to overtire or overexcite him, particularly in these early months, by trying to make him laugh too much.

18

Record of Growth

Weight
At one month

At two months

At three months

Length at three months

First smile

or by perpetually attracting his attention. The proper digestion of his food and his whole well being depends on a peaceful atmosphere, although ordinary household noises will not interphere with the deep, peaceful sleep of healthy babyhood.

Up to now baby's only food has been milk including orange juice, rosehip syrup or other preparations with a high vitamin C content. Now it is worthwhile developing new tastes. Any new food should be introduced very gradually and only one new one at a time. A teaspoonful of cereal with a little milk and sugar, later or some sieved vegetable or the yolk of a lightly boiled egg.

The modern tendency to look at the book of words instead of at baby denies him the extra mothering he needs on wakeful days. He may be lonely when not asleep and want the simple delight of your company. If the relationship between mother and child is to be a happy one there must be time for a little fussing and sympathetic understanding to provide for your baby the happiness and security of being loved, which is his deepest need from the beginning.

20

GENERAL PROGRESS

SNAPSHOTS

At Six Months

At six months the average baby will have doubled his birth weight and be gaining about a pound a month depending on his activity and previous weight.

With the first two teeth errupting in the front of the lower jaw, baby will begin to change from sucking to biting and weaning in the full sense of the word should commence. The whole process should be extremely gradual and it is most important that baby shall continue to enjoy his meals.

Milk remains the most important item of baby's diet and will still be needed for each feed. Leave the milk until last, after he has taken what he will of other food.

There is no point in forcing baby to take a new

RECORD OF GROWTH

Weight   At four months

At five months

At six months

Length at six months

Sat up alone

food he dislikes, but as soon as he shows any inclination let baby assist in feeding himself. He will make a mess but he will be much more interested in food when he is allowed to help himself. What baby eats each day should include something from the three main groups of food. Body-building proteins; energy-giving foods, rich in starch, sugar, fats, and the protective foods containing vitamins and minerals. This is what is meant by a varied, balanced diet.

From about three and a half months your baby should have regular times for exercise on a bed, or, if the weather is warm enough, in his pram. Free of all clothing except perhaps for a vest, he will feel encouraged to kick and to wave his arms about and be really energetic; though care should be taken that he does not get over tired or he may become fretful and end up in tears.

GENERAL PROGRESS

SNAPSHOTS

AT NINE MONTHS

THE average weight of a nine months old baby is about eighteen pounds. For sometime he has been able to sit up without support and may even try to stand with help and put one foot in front of another. He will coo and gurgle as he tries different sounds, and he may have attempted to say a word or two.

A playpen will give him plenty of opportunity to make his own experiments, and a place where he can be left alone in safety for short periods. A hard mattress placed inside the playpen and covered with a mackintosh sheet and a washable under blanket tied over it, not only keeps him out of floor draughts but will prevent baby hurting himself. Wooden beads on a string, woolly or rubber animals and a

30

RECORD OF GROWTH

Weight
At seven months

At eight months

At nine months

Length at nine months

First word

ball will keep him amused now that baby is far more alert and he will require less sleep.

Now it will be necessary to wash baby's hands constantly for he crawls, touches everything within his reach and then puts his hands in his mouth.

There will be four to eight teeth coming through and at this age baby looks forward to his meals. He can chew so the variety of foods can be widened. He can even share some of your own meals. But fried and fatty foods are rarely suitable and highly seasoned foods should certainly be avoided. A tiny slice of apple after eating is a good thing for this cleans his teeth naturally.

Baby's afternoon kicking time on the rug should be encouraged and outings in the pram will interest his rapidly developing brain. He will be quite fascinated by the changing scenery and the activity around him; he will return home contented and ready for tea and bed. Tucked up with a favourite toy he will quickly settle down.

GENERAL PROGRESS

SNAPSHOTS

The First Birthday

AT twelve months the average baby has tripled his birth weight and should weigh between twenty one and twenty two pounds. The average height is about twenty nine inches.

Baby will now be having three meals a day and be on a pleasantly varied diet. Finely minced lamb, chicken or rabbit, steamed white fish and grated cheese can usually be digested at a year.

Training a child to be clean and dry need not begin seriously until after weaning and early teething troubles are over, and may even be left until baby is a year old. The important thing to remember is that all emotion, either of pleasure or annoyance must be banished and a calm wholly dispassionate attitude adopted which takes for granted the child

36

RECORD OF GROWTH

Weight
At ten months

At eleven months

At one year

Height at one year

Number of teeth

will do what is expected of him. The year old child is an inquiring active little person so he will need plenty of rest and sleep. Try to keep on with two sleeps a day until baby finds it impossible, even then it is a good plan to let him rest either in his cot or in his pram in the garden.

His limbs are losing the baby curves and straightening out, he crawls to things he cannot reach, stands alone and may even attempt to walk. He will be saying a few words quite distinctly and can understand simple commands. At this age he can, as a rule, hold a cup to drink from and will help a little towards dressing himself by putting his arms and legs in the right place.

All this amazing progress in growth and movement has come about in the short space of one year, and it is through these experiences that your baby's mind grows. The pleasure in doing something new and difficult, his successes and failures are of the greatest importance to his mental development and personal happiness if he is to be the determined, strong minded youngster you want him to be.

GENERAL PROGRESS

SNAPSHOTS

CHART OF BABY'S AVERAGE WEIGHT

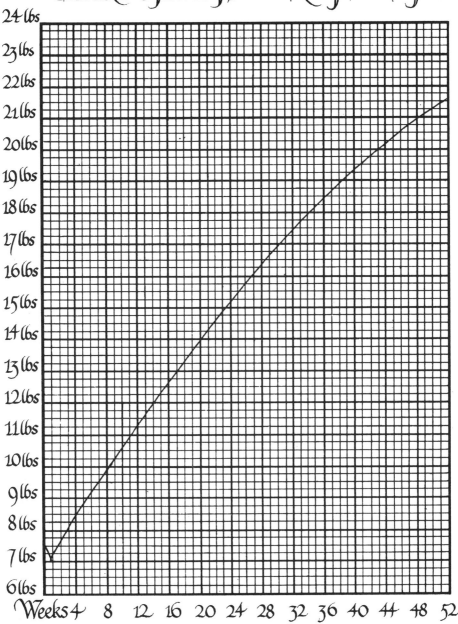

24 lbs	
23 lbs	
22 lbs	
21 lbs	
20 lbs	
19 lbs	
18 lbs	
17 lbs	
16 lbs	
15 lbs	
14 lbs	
13 lbs	
12 lbs	
11 lbs	
10 lbs	
9 lbs	
8 lbs	
7 lbs	
6 lbs	

Weeks 4   8   12   16   20   24   28   32   36   40   44   48   52

CARE of the TEETH

BABY'S first set of teeth were formed before birth but the age at which each tooth appears varies considerably and it is surprising how long they remain in the gums before they finally break through. There is no need to worry because late teething is rarely a sign of bad teeth, or early teething a sign of good ones. Hard crusts or rusks to bite are a great help when the teeth are coming through. A peeled whole apple cleans them as well as exercising the jaws.

Teething is not an ailment and being a perfectly normal process should not be accompanied by any trouble, in fact, you may find that baby has cut a tooth or two even in the midst of being good especially the first lower ones. But the double teeth are usually a little more difficult and there

Milk Teeth

Date _____

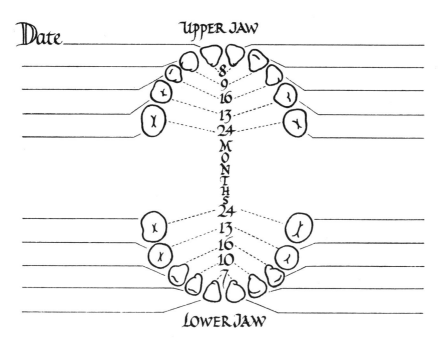

Upper Jaw

8
9
16
13
24
M O N T H S
24
13
16
10
7

Lower Jaw

Permanent Teeth

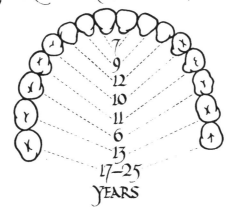

7
9
12
10
11
6
13
17—25
Years

43

may be a few restless nights when a back tooth is actually piercing the gum. If baby wakes in the night it is wise to change him, give him a cool drink of water, then put him back in his cot and leave him. Although baby needs extra sympathetic attention at this time it is fatal to establish bad habits which will have to be broken later, when he is too young to understand any explanations.

It is generally recognised that the proper structure of the permanent teeth depends for the most part on the amount of calcium and vitamin D, which is the calcium-activating vitamin. Vitamin C is also thought to be a considerable factor to good dentition. Therefore, from the very earliest age, until all his second teeth are through, it is important to see that baby has his daily ration of cod liver oil and orange juice.

Decay is usually the work of tiny organisms which thrive on food left in and between the teeth. Hence the necessity to brush the teeth regularly, beginning when baby has about eight teeth, with a small soft brush and using milk of magnesia as a dentifrice

When the child is three or four he should visit a dentist for an inspection, and continue at six-monthly intervals, or more frequently if the dentist considers it necessary.

RECORD OF BABY'S TEETH

First tooth appeared

First visit to the dentist

First tooth lost

Cutting of second teeth

Reactions during teething

45

THE FIRST STEPS

SOMEWHERE between twelve and eighteen months most babies will learn to walk even if they get no encouragement. Give baby plenty of opportunity to pull himself up in his playpen or cot, and to teach himself to walk from chair to chair. A little help will give him courage, so let him hold your finger, then he can leave go when he feels sufficiently confident.

Once the toddling stage is reached baby will need plenty of rest, because he is using a great deal of energy in walking and picking himself up after his tumbles. In these early days it is never wise to let him run about for more than an hour as he will get overtired and if he is heavy the bones of his legs may even become bowed. There should be times when baby sits in his pram to rest his legs.

THE FIRST STEPS

On the   day of   19

Age

Where

When the toddler is trotting about quite firmly on his feet indoors, let him walk for the last few minutes of his daily outing, when a pair of reins will be found very useful for keeping him from suddenly dashing into the road. A daily walk will give the two to three year old nearly all the exercise he requires, but if your child tires easily do not hesitate to let him have part of the outing in his pram. Apart from the exercise the walk will get him accustomed to change of scenery and the casual conversation of strangers.

A tendency to flat feet may be corrected by teaching the child to walk with his toes pointing very slightly inwards and by simple play-exercises such as walking on tip-toe and picking up a pencil or marble with his toes.

Throughout childhood the importance of well fitting shoes specially designed to allow for the healthy growth of young feet cannot be over emphasised.

48

SNAPSHOTS

49

AT EIGHTEEN MONTHS

AT eighteen months the average weight is around twenty four pounds and the average height is about thirty inches. A certain amount of routine is still important to the well-being of the toddler—a baby no longer. A little more time given to playing and less to sleeping; he likes to know what is going to happen during his day, to be able to take his place in the life of the family and he loves to help.

A well-fed child will nearly always have a sunny disposition, and sturdy growth depends on a well-balanced diet. The child who eats a lot is not necessarily well-fed, and it is not only the right kind of food that matters, a happy leisurely atmosphere at mealtimes is quite as important for his general health now that he is growing older, as it was for the new baby.

50

RECORD OF GROWTH

Weight At fourteen months

At sixteen months

At eighteen months

Height at eighteen months

By the time a child is eighteen months he will be running about quite steadily, though his sense of balance is not yet developed, and it is as well to be aware of some of the dangers of early childhood, such as burns or scalds, falls, street accidents, also the perils of river or pond for those who live near deep water. All reasonable steps should be taken to ensure against these.

The precautions will be the use of a safety harness to prevent falls out of the pram or high chair; by teaching the child to crawl forward up the stairs and to come down backwards, until he is old enough to walk up and down properly. From the time he is able to grab at things, utensils holding boiling, or even hot, liquid in any form whatever, should never be left within his reach, and fireguards are, of course, essential.

Apart from teaching your child how to look after himself, and from the very first showing him how and when to cross a road, the best safeguard is a continual awareness which keeps you subconsciously on the watch to see he is not heading for trouble. But there is a world of difference between panic and precaution and accidents do not easily happen to the child who is fearless and free.

52

GENERAL PROGRESS

SNAPSHOTS

The Second Birthday

WHEN a child reaches the age of two he should be approximately four times his original birth weight, and will now gain between four and six pounds yearly. Although his physical progress will not be as obvious as the rapid growth and development of the baby during the first year, it is always interesting and well worth recording at every birthday. As a rule boys weigh rather more than girls and are inclined to be taller.

During babyhood his very helplessness gave him first claim to his mother's attention, but by the time he is two he is showing signs of a will of his own which he is anxious to assert. There is so much he wants to do, yet he can achieve so little. He will get immense satisfaction if he is allowed and encouraged

56

RECORD OF GROWTH

Weight
    At twenty months

    At twenty two months

    At two years

Height at two years

General Progress

to do little things for himself. Let him pull off his socks and shoes, and wash his grubby knees himself; it will take longer, but it will be well worth while & in helping him to independence he will experience the sense of achievement.

It is sometimes a problem to know how to dress the active youngster who is never in one place for more than a few minutes, running in and out of the warm room to perhaps a chilly garden. Three woollen garments for indoors during the winter should be sufficient, adjusting gradually to cotton for the summer, and in really warm sunshine a brief sun-suit and hat is ideal.

Perhaps the most marked progress will be in the two year olds development of speech. Whereas at eighteen months he could say only a few words, at two he will be using simple sentences, and the three year old has a vocabulary of about a thousand words. Language has become a real means of communication and is of the greatest importance to him in his social development. He needs companions of his own age and likes to play with them.

During the ages of three and four there will be a perpetual stream of questions. He will want to know the whys and wherefores of everything around him

58

The Third Birthday

Weight (2 stone 5lbs)

Height (3 feet 1in)

General Progress

and his questions should be answered briefly and in words he can understand. To him the world is an exciting place and everything is thrilling in the extreme.

Helping with the household duties is great fun and if he is given a few little jobs which he can consider his own and are of real assistance, he will be delighted to take his share in the responsibility of the home. He is very conscious he is no longer a baby and as his physical skill increases he will like to show off his little feats of adventure and daring.

The four year old is usually open to reason and at this age he can begin to accept authority and understand the question of good and bad conduct. It is important not to make unnecessary demands. The real essentials give quite enough opportunity to teach the child obedience, and there is no reason why you should not make it as easy as possible for him to obey.

Speaking with pleasant and calm expectation that he will obey does much to win his co-operation, but his response is based most of all on his trust in you. Good manners need to be taught very carefully and

The Fourth Birthday

Weight (2 stone 9lbs)

Height (3 feet 5 ins)

General Progress

mainly by example— in a happy, casual and sympathetic atmosphere, for politeness and friendliness are the result of the youngster's feelings towards others. Without expecting too much of him too soon, he needs to be guided firmly while he is very young and still guided, but with decreasing firmness as he grows into a reasonably civilized way of life.

Through play the young child developes his initiative and his creative imagination is given scope. Since toys must play such an important part in the child's daily life, it is obviously necessary that he should be given the right material.

For the garden a low see-saw is ideal play material, or a horizontal bar on two upright posts within reach of the child's upstretched arms, if there is no tree on which to swing. He needs sand and water, a trowl and pail, and a few strong well-made toys, such as a little wheelbarrow or cart, a wooden animal on wheels, or an engine, and a ball. For indoors there should be dolls and animals coloured

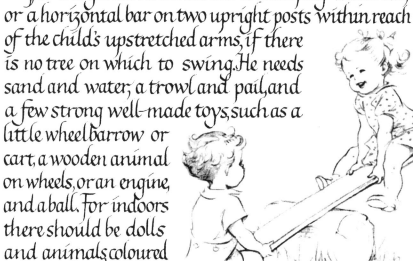

The Fifth Birthday

Weight (2 stone 13 lbs)

Height (3 feet 7 ins)

General Progress

crayons and large sheets of paper to draw on, plasticine a few easy jig saws, some building bricks, and several well selected picture and simple story books.

With the fifth birthday the child has reached school age, and as schools vary considerably, it is most important that parents should make themselves thoroughly familiar with the school before sending the child there. He may ask questions about letters and counting at an even earlier age, and there is no harm in answering his questions if he shows a desire to learn, but the child must be allowed to develop his abilities at his own pace.

The beginning of the sixth year is the normal age at which the child will best learn to read, but it is advisable to make sure he can do this before he is seven and if necessary, help him at home, or he will not be able to understand what is written on the board.

The first seven years of a child's life are the most impressionable, and caring for a child is a great

responsibility but if parents can be wise and patient through these early years, and give every opportunity to the child to develop soundly, a very firm foundation has been laid for a stable personality.

THE SIXTH BIRTHDAY

Weight (3 stone 4lbs)

Height (3feet 9ins)

General Progress

SNAPSHOTS

THE SEVENTH BIRTHDAY

Weight (3 stone 9 lbs)

Height (3 feet 10 ins)

General Progress

SNAPSHOTS

THE SICK CHILD

SIGNS of illness are a temperature above normal, fretfulness, pain, rash on the chest, the back or face, shivering & sickness. Call the doctor if the usual remedies of light diet and rest do not bring an improvement within twenty four hours, or sooner if the child's condition rapidly worsens.

When a child is ill and particularly if he has to be in bed for several weeks it is well worth considering if he can be brought downstairs and nursed in a room on the ground floor. As well as providing the little patient with more interests he will not be so shut away, and a sick child should never be left where he cannot be easily heard and constantly watched.

If possible choose a sunny room with a large window and an open fireplace to keep plenty of fresh air circulating in the room. The bed or cot should be in a corner and not in a direct draught between the fireplace and window or between window and door.

Without over-protecting a child certain preventive precautions should be taken against the more serious infectious diseases. Vaccination against smallpox and immunisation against diphtheria are proved successes. Protection can be given against whooping cough, polio, tetanus and the typhoid group, also against tuberculosis. Some of these inoculations are given together; others should be repeated before a child starts school. It takes time for an infectious disease to develop and show itself, so if a child has been in contact with another who is known to have one of these complaints he should not mix with other children, but be kept in quarantine until the incubation period is over and so be sure that he has not contracted the disease.

A separate room must be used when nursing an infectious case, and utensils and cutlery used in the room should be washed up separately. The mother or nurse attending the child need not be isolated from the rest of the family if she wears an overall in the sick room and removes it when leaving. The hands should be washed in weak lysol everytime she leaves the room.

Everything should be done to make the time in bed pass quickly and happily, but toys and books must be burned when the illness is over.

The incubation periods are as follows—

Chicken-pox	21 days
Diphtheria	10 days
Measles	15 days
Mumps	25 days
Scarlet fever	10 days
Smallpox	14 days
Whooping cough	21 days

VACCINATION AND IMMUNISATION

ILLNESSES

SCHOOL RECORD

FIRST DRAWING AND WRITING

FUNNY SAYINGS AND INCIDENTS

Favourite Books

PETS AND PLAYMATES

FAVOURITE GAMES

PRAYERS